BELLA, THE QUEEN BEE

JULIAN POPESCU

CAVALIER PAPERBACKS

Published by Cavalier Paperbacks 1998
Burnham House
Jarvis St
Upavon
Wilts SN9 6DU

ISBN 1-899470-06-9

Printed and bound in Great Britain by Cox &
Wyman, Reading, Berkshire

CONTENTS

CONTENTS

CHAPTER ONE

THE CASTLE

There was once an old Queen Bee who lived with her subjects in a hive that was in a meadow surrounded by tall hedges and trees. The meadow was at its best in the spring sunshine. The trees, mostly sycamore and oak, looked proud dressed in their new yellowish-green foliage. A horse chestnut held its white candles pointing at the sky.

Down below there were buttercups and dandelions, daisies and primroses scattered among grass, cow parsley and nettles. The flowers shook their heads in the gentle breeze and nodded greetings to each other sprinkling puffs of pollen around them. Bees full of zest and energy hovered over their scented heads, alighting gently and licking the nectar with their long tongues. Other rivals, bumble bees and hover flies, were also after the sweet liquid which had been freshly prepared that morning by the flowers for the benefit of their winged visitors.

After they had their fill, the bees flew in a straight line to their hive perched on two stones on the left hand side of the meadow. The hive was almost obscured by the evergreen bushes growing behind it. Painted in light blue, it had a white roof and four turrets decorated with gold leaf which made it look like a castle. A royal standard, no larger than a postage stamp, fluttered in the middle signalling to the world outside that the Queen was in residence.

Two white pillars adorned the entrance to the hive that had double walls. The tops of the pillars were shaped like an exotic leaf and were surmounted on either side by a shield bearing the coat of arms consisting of two wings and a pair of crossed stings. The shield was painted red with yellow stripes. Beneath was a scroll on which was inscribed the motto, "WHERE BEES ARE, THERE IS HONEY."

WHERE BEES ARE · THERE IS HONEY

The alighting board of wood at the entrance to the hive sloped at an angle of about twenty degrees to make it easier for the bees to land when laden with nectar or pollen. Already the guard bees in their yellow striped uniforms and red berets were pacing to and fro checking the incomers and even frisking any bees suspected of smuggling drugs or poisons taken from the flowers of poppies or the deadly nightshade.

Inside the hive the scent of honey and freshly made wax filled every nook and cranny. Steep passages led upwards between the waxen walls of the brood chamber full of combs with six sided cells crammed with larvae and nymphs about to be transformed into real worker bees – these would number about 40,000 in late May. Behind the brood cells were the larders used for storing honey and pollen. Next to the larders were the kitchens where royal jelly, pickled pollen and bee bread were made.

Half way up the main combs was an open space, dimly lit, surrounded by pillars of wax topped by crowns and shields. The floor looked like polished marble. This was the royal chamber where the Queen Bee held royal court. Twice the size of an ordinary bee because she had been fed on royal jelly, Queen Bella wore a cloak brilliantly striped in yellow. She also had a crown on her head made of sugar crystals that sparkled as she moved along.

Twelve ladies-in-waiting always surrounded the Queen. They were chosen from the very young bees and gingerly kept their distance but always faced their Sovereign. From time to time they offered their Queen honey cake and other sweet morsels on a waxen platter. The Queen snatched the food and ate it smacking her mandibles noisily. She looked up at her sundial; the hour had come for the day's main business.

Queen Bella gave several shrill hoots and suddenly there was silence all round. The assembled bees stopped work and their continual buzzing and stood to attention to listen to the voice of their Queen issue the proclamation, "Today, I am told by my scouts, the weather is warm and dry. There are only a few clouds and no rain is forecast. Go out and fetch fifty thousand droplets of nectar and ten thousand bags of pollen. We need drinking water to replenish our tanks. Draw water from the pond because it is clean and safe. We need several grains of propolis or green glue from buds and the backs of leaves to stick combs together and seal cracks. These are my orders for today. Go, worker bees and do your duty."

Hardly had these words been uttered than a high-pitched sound like a fanfare of trumpets filled the hive. The bees sang their anthem of praise to the Queen. A general excitement then spread from bee to bee as they touched each other with their antennas. Marching orders were issued by the supervisors to each of their sections. As if by magic, thousand upon thousand of bees trooped out of the hive and flew in ever widening circles until they calculated their

exact bearings. Then they flew in a straight
line at their chosen target.

Some of the bees carried tiny buckets slung on their shoulders to draw water from the nearby pond. Others flew to flowers they knew by instinct were laden with pollen. The bees opened the baskets they carried strapped to their legs, scooped up the yellow grains of pollen and poured them into the baskets. The main troop of bees made for a field of rape blossom, gleaming brilliantly on a hill-side where gallons of nectar awaited them.

The bees returned with the fruits of their labour in a steady stream to the hive. As they arrived others were leaving and often they bumped into each other at the entrance, spilling their baskets of pollen or slopping their buckets of water. The cleaners came and tidied things up and work resumed as normal.

The drones or male bees formed a privileged class by themselves. They were excused all work and could feed at will on the nectar or honey they found in the cells. They had large bulging eyes, bushy eyebrows, long antennae, hairy chests and fat bellies. When they flew about their buzz was louder and hoarser than that of the other bees. They were, however, expected to escort the Queen if she went out on a flight which she seldom did and not without good reason.

The young drones wore a grey waistcoat and a bow tie. The older drones were formally dressed in dark clothes. They all belonged to flying clubs since drones were expected to be good aerobatic fliers. They had formed squadrons of nine of which each had a distinctive colouring, red, yellow or blue. While flying across the meadow and adjoining common which was a sea of buttercups at this time of the year, the drones had caught sight of human hang-gliders and micro-light fliers who came from a small disused airfield two and a half kilometres away. The drones admired the human fliers very much and talked about them at length.

When drones were out flying, they often competed in aerobatics but they never alighted on a flower or twig to rest. They were bound by the strict rules of their club to keep on flying and they alighted only when they returned home to the hive.

Unlike the worker bees, drones carried no sting in their tail and so could never do guard duty or engage in combat with intruders. The drones regarded fighting as a boring occupation, slightly beneath their dignity and best left to the worker bees. But they enjoyed watching the guardian bees sting to death any robber bees, ants, moths or other insects which happened to trespass into the hive.

CHAPTER TWO

A GOOD DAY'S WORK

Young worker bees, below the age of two weeks, were not sent out to forage. Instead, they carried out various duties inside the hive, cleaning cells, feeding the larvae in their nurseries, taking turns in the kitchens and keeping the brood chamber warm. Young bees were very sensitive to cold and could easily die if they became chilled.

For this reason the temperature in the chamber was never allowed to fall below 20°C. Humidity, too, had to be strictly controlled, for too much damp gave the bees aches and pains and made the wax crumble.

But the rest of the bees toiled all day long without rest until they fulfilled their orders. Some of the worker bees even brought in more nectar and pollen than was expected of them. They worked from sunrise to sunset, belonged to no unions and never went on strike or lost their temper. They learnt from birth that "DILIGENCE IS THE MOTHER OF GOOD FORTUNE."

The nectar brought in by the bees in their honey sac was discharged into storage cells where it was mixed with a tiny quantity of poison from the sting to preserve it. Some of the nursing bees helped the foragers with this task lapping up the regurgitated nectar and placing it in the cells themselves.

The pollen came in various colours, yellow, red or black and was poured into special cells to be later prepared as bread for the hungry larvae. The larvae would start to spin their cocoons and would turn into nymphs. This would take just over a week. A few days after that they would complete their metamorphosis or transformation and so become bees.

DILIGENCE IS the MOTHER of GOOD FORTUNE!

In the meantime, worker bees returning from their visits to local flowers, flapped their wings and danced the round or the waggle to indicate to their sisters the exact location of the flowers. All the bees could easily receive this message if they had been properly taught. For this was an important ritual in their daily life that saved bees much time in their search for nectar-bearing flowers. As the sun settled on the horizon in a red glow and the shadows of the trees lengthened by the minute across the meadow, the bees were back in the hive going through their roll calls. Twenty were reported missing that day, presumably dead of exhaustion by the way side.

Several bees had fallen in the pond and drowned while others had been caught by swifts on the wing and died a terrible death.

The Queen was pleased with the day's work and went round inspecting the large number of cells filled with nectar and pollen. Then she started to lay eggs by the thousand in the outlying combs.

As darkness fell, a gentle hum could be heard coming from the hive. The air around the hive was filled with the sweet smell of honey and pollen and attracted moths which hovered around in the hope of finding an easy way into the hive. A hedgehog passed by sniffing the air and sighing at the thought of so much tempting sweetness.

Inside the hive the night's work was about to begin. Worker bees carried out repairs to cells or helped with odd jobs in the nurseries. The worst task was removing the dead bodies of fluffy baby bees. Some old bees with missing legs or broken wings had to be led out to die of exposure in the cold night air since their useful life was at an end.

Worker bees belonged to several crafts such as foragers, builders and nurses.

The builders carried out repairs to cells. They also fetched tiny slabs of wax which they used to build new cells in readiness for the nectar to be collected in the days ahead. Also cells that were full of honey, had to be capped with a fine layer of wax. The wax-making bees hung in a tight cluster to keep themselves uncomfortably warm. The honey they chose to eat was heated and concentrated in their glands. They sweated it out and the sweat became wax.

Meanwhile the drones gorged themselves on nectar and then complained about its quality. Some said it was too sugary while others complained about it tasting too bland. They were even fed by nursing bees on a mixture of nectar and pollen which was full of vitamins. Two drones in particular, Tom and Harold, were well known for their complaints. "All we get is nectar from rape flowers. It's got no taste at all," Tom added smacking his chops.

After their grumbles, the drones invariably got into the way of the workers. They boasted about their handsome looks and privileges, expected the worker bees to make way for them and made rude remarks about males being superior to females. "We have all the brains and talents because of our big heads while you have all the muscle," said one of the drones called Billy by his mates.

Another drone chimed in : "The bees are old bags and silly cows."

Many of the worker bees cleaning the floors overheard the comment of the drones and

burst out in an angry buzz which translated into English meant:

"Did you hear that, sissies? Who do they think they are, those silly drones? Let's call the supervisor."

"What's up?" the supervisor asked, adjusting her glasses. "If you drones don't shut up and leave the workers alone, I'll give you a sting where it hurts!"

The drones tried to deny the allegations made against them, but the supervisor had deaf ears and showed them her sting which was already dripping with poison.

"Help, buddies, we're going to be hurt by that nasty supervisor!" Billy shouted, his voice trembling with fear. Billy and the other drones then hastily withdrew to their corners and carried on grumbling in whispers until they fell asleep.

CHAPTER THREE

THE ENEMY AT THE GATE

April showers were followed by May flowers. The sun shone brightly and warmed up the earth. The hedges were sprinkled with the white blossom of the hawthorn while the sycamore trees were festooned with sprigs of pale green flowers showering the air with pollen. The chestnut trees proudly displayed their white or red blossom, while in the nearby orchard, surrounded by prickly hedges, the cherry blossom was nearly over and the early varieties of apple trees began to burst forth in rosy petals.

The air was full of scented vapours rising

from the earth. Clouds of mosquitoes and midges rose and fell with the prevailing breeze. The bees, meanwhile, were hard at work gathering in the plentiful supplies of nectar and pollen remembering the old saying that it was better to wear out than rust out.

Inside the hive Queen Bella, wrapped in her yellow striped cloak, was given regular reports about the quantity and quality of the nectar being stored. She was told that a whole generation of young bees had hatched out and were already undergoing training for their days of hard work ahead. Foraging for nectar could take them a kilometre or two cross-country away from the hive and they had to learn the best and shortest routes home.

The guards paced up and down the alighting board checking the returning bees to see that there were no intruders. Some dark native bees from a hive about a kilometre away tried to sneak into the hive and steal honey, but they were intercepted just in time and sent packing. The guards were soon joined by five or six professional fanners who flapped their wings at the entrance to the hive to ventilate and refresh the air inside.

The first change of the guards watched by a crowd of bees took place around noon. The late morning had been quiet, and all round, the aroma of ripening nectar into honey could be felt. The sky was blue as far as the eye could see and the heat of the sun made everyone drowsy.

The inter-city railway line was barely a kilometre away, and trains which had been speeded-up of late, roared as they went by at hourly intervals. The passage of trains, though it shook the earth at times, made no impression on the bees. Their ears and antennae were more sensitive to the more homely signals of nature. A distant buzz, low and regular in tone could be heard. It came and went. It was not the quick buzz of bees or the restless and impatient noise of the bumble-bee. The sound had something sinister about it. Several guards pricked their ears and stretched their antennae, moving them round in circles like radar. The guards in the front line looked up in alarm.

Suddenly a large shape appeared. After making several circles, it landed on the alighting board with a thump. It was a hornet. Displaying its elegant red and yellow colours and swishing its deadly tail it made for the entrance to the hive with arrogant strides. The fanners took fright and disappeared inside while a shout went up among the guards. "Robber at the entrance. We are attacking the enemy."

An angry cluster of guards threw themselves upon the hornet. Two or three were quickly stabbed and left to stagger away in deadly pain. Another guard had her head lopped off by the hornet's strong mandibles. Then, still undaunted, the hornet looked for a way of getting into the stores in the brood chamber. Meanwhile a ring of guards surrounded the enemy, their drawn daggers glinting with poison. Soon the buzzing sounds of alarm inside the hive grew into a deafening crescendo and scores of bees swarmed out onto the alighting board.

Confusion reigned at first. Bees pushed each other over and even fought among themselves. The hornet arched itself and raised its wings, looking like a dragon. Bravely the bees advanced on it. Some clutched its wings, others took hold of its legs. The guards stabbed at the hornet's belly with their jagged daggers. Several thrusts penetrated the enemy's protective scales. The hornet fought viciously and several more guards fell. At last after much heaving and puffing, the hornet, giddy and poisoned by the stings of bees, swayed under the weight of his attackers. The sting in his tail continued to stab the air at random. Then, overcome by the unequal contest, the hornet slumped at the entrance and lay dead. The bees angrily lifted his body out of the hive and into the grass below.

It was some time after this emergency that the bees calmed down. The guards continued to be jittery as they resumed their stations. They checked and frisked all incoming bees with great care. Some of the guards took off and flew in circles ready to report the approach of any unwelcome guest.

The fanners returned to work at the entrance. Other bees swept and cleared up the alighting board of all the debris from the fight. Two messengers were sent to report in detail to Queen Bella telling her of the outcome of the hornet's raid and giving her the casualty list. The Queen sighed as she heard the names called out and how her subjects had died. She hooted several times with pleasure as she was told again and again about the self-sacrifice and bravery of the guards on duty. She rejoiced at their victory and then sent back a royal message thanking all for doing their duty so bravely and ended by reminding them of the old saying, "HE THAT STEALS HONEY SHOULD BEWARE OF THE STING."

CHAPTER FOUR

THE BIG STORM

It had rained for several days. The ground was soggy and large puddles were everywhere. The trees were dripping wet and their branches hung down in misery. The flowers in the field closed their petals and went to sleep. There was little work for the bees to do in such weather. They could not forage when it rained and even if the weather was clear but still wet, the bees could not risk contact with water which damaged their wings and fine hairs. So the mood in the brood chamber was very edgy. Nectar and honey were being consumed at all times of the day. The drones could not be persuaded to take less and recklessly sucked nectar out of cells regardless of the needs of others. There were many young mouths to feed. The worker bees were worried as there was no hope of re-stocking their supplies immediately.

Worker bees do not like being idle. They can become angry at the slightest thing. Quarrels were frequent as were the insults. The enforced idleness, due to the bad weather, also made the bees restless at night. They could not sleep and wandered about the passage-ways in search of something to do. They chatted for long spells with their sisters. Bees speak to each other with the help of their antennae. Soon they talked about the need for change. One said, "The Queen Bee has ruled for three years. She is too domineering and has a bad temper."

Another said, "She has over-ruled her councillors on too many matters of domestic and foreign policy."

"Yes, a new Virgin Queen might improve

things and get rid of some of those ghastly drones."

Unknown to these bees though, a group of rebel worker bees were already building an acorn shaped cell which could be used for rearing a Virgin Queen.

Though wet, the night was quiet. A few bats flew about in their crazy fashion and then disappeared. Midnight came and went. Only a slight wind ruffled the leaves of the surrounding trees. Branches were hanging down heavily laden not only with leaves but also with acorns and seed pods.

But in the early hours of the morning the wind grew stronger and started to whistle and hiss through the trees, gusting at times up to 100km an hour.

The hive was well protected by bushes and young trees at the rear and all the bees could hear was the wind roaring high above in the trees. Then suddenly the hive was rocked by a thud. A leafy branch from a nearby tree spun down and hit the roof of the hive. Alarmed by the noise, the bees crowded out in the dark to investigate.

By then the wind was howling and tugging like a vandal at the branches and bushes. Next an almighty crack was heard and the branch from a huge oak, in the middle of the meadow, tumbled down snapping in two several smaller trees as it fell. The bees withdrew into the hive in a state of panic and stayed there.

The wind continued unabated in its fury until daylight when calm returned. Then the bees looked out of their hive and eyed a scene of devastation which they had never seen before. Trees that had stood proudly for centuries were uprooted and lying on the ground. Branches, twigs and leaves were strewn everywhere. The entrance to the hive was partially blocked by a heap of twigs and leaves. And two humans wearing Wellies and anoraks were walking about, as if in a daze, looking at the disaster area.

The bees formed long chains to pull away the leaves and twigs which were blocking the entrance to the hive. Finally they managed to clear several passages so that fresh air could get into the hive. Scouts were sent out to investigate the situation.

The quiet and peace of the hive was again disturbed that morning by the deafening sound of a chain saw. A human helped by two younger humans was sawing the branches of a fallen tree and then logging them. A cloud of sawdust filled the air while the humans picked up the logs and put them in a wheelbarrow. They then pushed the load to a shed by the farmhouse.

One of the younger humans approached the hive in search of twigs and branches. The guards on duty mistook the human for an intruder and decided to attack.

They buzzed angrily around its head. Soon one of the guards became entangled in fair hair. The bee felt trapped so she pulled out her sting and stabbed the warm pink flesh below. A yell of pain went up as the young human fluffed her hair in a vain attempt to get rid of the bee.

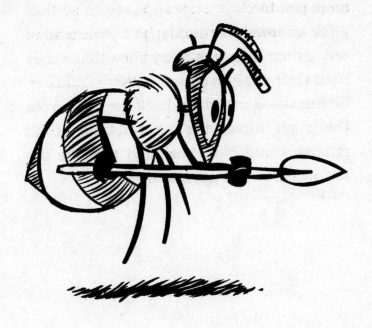

"I've been stung by a bee! Help somebody," she cried. The older human rushed to her rescue, parted the fair hair and pulled out the bee which by now was half-dead. He scraped the sting out with his nail. "Don't you go near that hive again," he said. "The bee that stung you has lost her sting and is now dying. Keep away if you don't want any more trouble."

The guards were saddened by the loss of one of their numbers. They knew that if they used their sting on a human they would die. No bee could ever draw back her sting from the tough human flesh. Yet not one of the guards would have hesitated to make the sacrifice if called upon to do so.

CHAPTER FIVE

CAUGHT RED-HANDED

It was a cold and starry night. The new moon, a slim crescent high in the sky, spread a feeble and uncertain light over the meadow. A moorhen by the pond uttered a cry as if a predator had startled her. A barn owl flew across the meadow and settled in a yew tree. Its plaintive hooting was re-echoed by another owl some distance away. Then all was silent again.

The bees had had a tiring day and were still busy clearing away shreds of old wax, balls of discarded pollen and the constant mess from the nurseries. Everything was put into bins ready for next morning's collection. Driven inside the brood chamber by the cold, the guards were huddled together and chatted from time to time to the sister bees.

"It's a dark night and all looks quiet," said one of the guards, shaking her legs.

"It's a bit boring standing here with nothing to do. I wish we could play a game of cards to while the time away," said another guard.

"What do you think the weather will do tomorrow?" asked one of the sister bees.

"I expect it will be a bright day because the sun set in a blaze of red and when that happens, you know the saying, RED NIGHT, SHEPHERD'S DELIGHT," answered a third guard who had just come in and overheard the chatter.

Little stirred outside the hive. A slug climbed onto the alighting board and left a slimy trail as it went by to disappear into the growth behind. Hardly visible, two shady and furtive figures with pincers in their tails appeared in front of the hive. They were earwig brothers drawn by the sweet smell of fresh wax and honey. They paused and listened. Then seeing the entrance unguarded, they sneaked inside the hive which was still and unusually quiet. Nothing moved in the pitch darkness.

The two earwigs went forward on tiptoes adjusting their face masks as they moved along the left-hand passage way. They searched several cells but found them empty. They went on quietly until they came to a cell full of nectar which they started to gobble up greedily.

As they made their way back they stumbled across a heap of granulated honey which they scooped up and put into the bags they carried.

Suddenly a bee patrol appeared on the scene and before the two robbers could make their getaway they were pinned down to the ground and hand-cuffed.

Hauled before a makeshift court, the earwigs could not deny that they had stolen nectar and honey for traces of nectar were still on their jaws and feet and their stomachs were bulging with the stuff. The hard evidence lay in the bags they had been caught with. They whined pitifully and begged for mercy. But bees are not used to showing mercy. They only know the harsh laws which have to be obeyed and applied to the letter.

The leader of the guards who was also the judge, pronounced the two robber earwigs guilty of pre-meditated theft on the evidence before her. She ordered their summary execution forthwith. There could be no appeal.

The two earwigs were bundled outside onto the alighting board. A crowd of bees followed to watch the execution. The two robbers were spread-eagled on the floor and stung to death.

After they were pronounced dead, worker bees came onto the scene and licked all the nectar off the corpses of the two earwigs. "WASTE NOT, WANT NOT," said one of the bees with obvious satisfaction. The bodies of the dried up earwigs were then thrown into the grass below as a warning to other would-be thieves. No more thefts were reported that night.

CHAPTER SIX

THE DUEL

As the summer months went by, Queen Bella saw her population grow and grow. There was hardly room in the hive for all the bees and many were forced to cluster outside at night-time to keep warm. They felt homeless and went about doing their chores with discontent on their faces. Older bees, too, muttered about the pace of work and lack of rest periods. They held meetings in secret at which they complained about the inflexible rule of the Queen Bee.

In the meantime, the group or rebel bees had finished building their acorn shaped cell in a quiet corner of the hive in which they now placed a fertilised egg stolen from the brood chamber. This particular egg grew and

developed in a special way because it was fed on a rich diet of royal jelly. After a week or so it was obvious to all that a new queen was being hatched. And when she was ready to come out of the acorn cell, the bees would clear away the fine wax capping to help her on the way. The bees would call her Virgin Queen or Princess.

Queen Bella was told by her trusted ladies-in-waiting that a plot was afoot to replace her with a new queen. Enraged by this information, Queen Bella searched the hive high and low for any tell-tale acorn shaped cells. She found two but they were empty. She gave up searching in despair. Then one morning she heard the unmistakable high-pitched call of her rival. The Virgin Queen was ready to challenge Queen Bella to a duel.

The whole hive prepared with great enthusiasm for the fight. An arena had been prepared in the middle of the brood chamber. Urged on by their supporters, Queen Bella and the Princess came face to face for the first time. They gnashed their jaws and traded insults, which caused uproar among the spectators. They both unsheathed their stings and got ready for mortal combat. Then with a cry of bravado, the Princess hurled herself at Queen Bella and they both became locked together, turning and twisting and making desperate attempts to plunge their deadly sting into each other's flesh. Bees from both camps cheered on the two combatants with frantic buzzing noises.

Being larger and heavier, Queen Bella had the advantage of weight on her side and she floored her opponent several times. The Princess was more nimble and slender and she ran in circles round Queen Bella. Suddenly the Princess grabbed Queen Bella from behind and held her tight. A deadly hush descended on the arena. Would the Queen receive the fatal sting? The almost stricken Queen Bella arched herself in one last desperate attempt and sent the Princess reeling backwards. A roar of applause broke the silence.

The fight lasted several more minutes and

there were moments of life and death but no clear advantage was scored by Queen Bella or her challenger. A draw was the only result that the seconds and the judges could agree on. The Princess had survived the ordeal against all the odds and was now admiringly called Princess Vanessa. A crowd of bees carried her away on their shoulders chanting all the way.

Queen Bella spruced herself up and once again surrounded by her ladies-in-waiting went in procession to her royal chamber followed by the majority of older bees. She was cheered several times and given extra food. Then she consulted her advisers about what to do next. It now became clear that the hive was a divided realm, the old bees siding with Queen Bella and the young bees following Princess Vanessa. This problem had to be solved in some other way than by force of arms.

In great secrecy, Queen Bella went to consult a wise old bee who knew something about astrology which she claimed had a bearing not only on human lives but also on the lives of bees.

"I want to make an important decision," Queen Bella told the astrologer bee. "Can you tell me the best date for this decision?"

"Your Majesty, you were born on 28 August, a time of year when the sun is near the stars called the Virgo constellation, the sixth sign of the Zodiac. According to my calculations, you are a Virgo, a person who is a perfectionist, down to earth but prone to accidents. Therefore you must avoid bad weather. Choose a day that is sunny and warm," urged the astrologer, taking in a deep breath, "and you will be lucky."

Queen Bella was much impressed with the advice of her astrologer. She had not revealed the purpose of her question or what she had in mind. Yet the advice was sound and fitted very well with her future plans.

CHAPTER SEVEN

THE EXODUS

Queen Bella received regular weather forecasts from her scouts. She knew, for instance, that the next two days were going to be wet and unsettled which meant that bees would not be able to forage and would be cooped up inside. The overcrowded hive was now rife with rumours about the health of Queen Bella and the alleged vitality of Princess Vanessa who was keeping a quiet profile for the time being.

Much disturbed by the presence of her rival in the hive, Queen Bella took important security measures. She placed guards round her chamber and sent spies into the other camp to find out what plots were being hatched. The fear of being murdered in her sleep was ever present in the old Queen. She remembered the history of her Grandmother who had been the victim of a palace plot.

Queen Bella held crown councils with her ladies-in-waiting and councillors. The first important decision taken was for all loyal bees to eat as much honey as they could.

"See to it that their bellies are full," she insisted. The second decision, which was treated as a great state secret, was to fix a date for Queen Bella to leave the hive followed by her loyal subjects, the older bees. The operation was code-named "EXODUS", otherwise known as swarming, and its first object was to find another realm where Queen Bella could rule in peace and quiet.

The older bees sensed that something important was afoot when the word got round for them to eat all the honey they could manage. As they became full, the bees felt reluctant to go out foraging and for the first time in their busy lives they just waited for something to happen. Some of the bees were a bundle of nerves and very excitable. They rushed hither and thither, went out of the hive and flew in circles.

The third day of this state of turmoil in the hive promised to be sunny and warm. The sky was a hazy blue from one end of the horizon to the other. The Queen remembered the prophecy of her astrologer and realised that the decisive moment had come. She put on her crown, grabbed the royal sceptre and gave her subjects the signal to go. In a flash the loyal bees separated from the rest of the hive and mustered at the entrance. They tripped over each other as they rushed out in a mass exodus that no force could hold back any more. A prolonged roar went up inside the brood chamber. Overcome by enthusiasm and joy, the bees pushed and jostled each other as they rushed down gangways and cat walks. Thousands of bees filled the air outside the hive making ever wider circles.

When Queen Bella emerged in her splendid attire she was blinded for a few seconds by the brilliant sun. She paced for an instant on the alighting board as if to say farewell to her old abode and then took off majestically across the meadow flying higher and higher followed by her subjects. The swarming bees sounded like an orchestra playing the first movement of a Brahms Symphony and it could be heard for miles around.

At first the swarm drifted aimlessly like a dark cloud. It clustered on the branches of an ash tree for a few minutes. The bees could not find Queen Bella in their midst so they took off again. The scouts searched frantically for their beloved Queen fearing the worst. Then they spotted her circling over a pear tree in the middle of the orchard and called to the others and soon the swarm had closed ranks around her. Settling among the branches of the pear tree, the seething cluster of bees looked like a huge upside-down pear so heavy that they bent the branches of the old tree.

Several hours passed before the scouts returned to report to Queen Bella that they had found an empty hive. The swarm led by the Queen this time rose from the tree in a hurry and followed the path traced by the forward scouts. Soon they arrived in the rear garden of a council house where an empty hive stood propped against a brick and flint wall.

The entrance to the hive had been carelessly left open, so the bees took possession. Once they were in the hive and were sure that the Queen was with them, they started to chase away the spiders and moths and clear the cobwebs. They killed several wax moths. Next they cleaned up the combs in the brood chamber. Already bees were coming in laden with nectar and pollen. Queen Bella was pleased with her new home though she thought it was not quite so grand as the one she had left behind.

CHAPTER EIGHT

THE SLAUGHTER

After the mass exodus, the Virgin Queen, Vanessa, looked in dismay around the brood chamber. Her rival and the departing bees had taken several pounds of prime honey with them. The bees left behind, though still numerous, were young and inexperienced. They showed little respect for the Virgin Queen who had to make do without her usual followers. The explanation for this state of affairs was simple. A queen that could not have offspring was of little use to the hive. The Virgin Queen now felt the urgent and pressing need to have a royal wedding.

A proclamation was issued that the Princess Vanessa would take a husband. The news caused great excitement among the drones who started to buzz around and shout about their virility at the top of their voices. Princess Vanessa, dressed in her wedding gown, made her way to the exit. As she took off she almost became entangled in her bridal veils. Then she noticed drones in hot pursuit on all sides. The Virgin Queen soared up into the air, then dived and circled around. She felt elated and excited. She flew so fast that the drones could hardly keep up with her. One drone managed to fly higher than the Virgin Queen. Then like a dive bomber he homed on the virgin, picked her roughly in his claws and thrust himself deeply into her body. He flapped his wings in triumph and moved away only to feel a seering pain in his stomach.

The unlucky drone was none other than Harold. True to nature, he had left his organ implanted in the body of Princess Vanessa and his life ebbed away as she returned to the hive. And now the bees noticed that their Queen was not a virgin any more. They set about cleaning and nursing her with all the respect due to a fertile queen. Then the bees sang a coronation hymn and proclaimed their new sovereign Queen Vanessa.

The new Queen started laying eggs in the following days. And so the future of the hive was assured though the bees were angered one morning to see some of their best honey taken away by the large human who owned the meadow. To add insult to injury he used smoke to frighten the bees when he opened up the hive to remove the honeycombs.

After this distressing event, Queen Vanessa saw with satisfaction that her young subjects had learnt the art of foraging and were now bringing in nectar and pollen. As the summer days grew shorter and autumn approached, the quantity of nectar and pollen brought in by the bees began to diminish. Anxious eyes were now looking at the state of the stores. Some of the professional bees calculated that 25kg of honey were needed by the hive's population to survive the winter in comfort. The stock of honey was at present below this safety level and a large number of drones continued to feed in a reckless way.

Queen Vanessa consulted her council about the problem of the drones. In keeping with tradition, the council advised the merciless slaughter of all drones before the end of the month. The Queen personally issued the proclamation, "ALL DRONES ARE TO BE EXECUTED."

News of the proclamation was at first dismissed with incredulity by the drones but soon they realised that the other bees really did mean business. Drones that took off for a stroll were denied entry when they returned to the alighting board and were viciously pushed overboard and left to struggle to their death in the wet grass. The more artful drones who stayed behind and hid in dark corners were picked up one by one, then their wings were clipped and they were bundled outside and left to die of exposure.

Finally, young strong drones who could put up a fight were stung and so killed without mercy by the bees. In one single week, the hive was rid of well over a hundred drones. The stock of honey for the coming winter was safe for the time being.

CHAPTER NINE

WINTER

In the old hive the life of the bees returned to normal. As August gave way to September, the clover dried up and there were less and less flowers about, yet the bees continued to forage as if driven by an unseen hand. They even searched for honey in fruit-juices and other left-overs on garden tables and chairs. Their instinct told them that winter was approaching and they had to be prepared for weeks and even months when they could do no work. Queen Vanessa laid as many eggs as she could afford to strengthen the hive's population for the cold days ahead.

By the end of September, the hive was in good shape. There were neat rows of sealed honeycombs and plenty of pickled pollen, that is to say pollen mixed with honey. The hive's population had grown two-fold since the departure of the old Queen so when it was cold the bees could cluster closely and keep warm. Queen Vanessa spent more and more time with her ladies-in-waiting and retinue who saw to it that their cherished ruler was well fed and warm.

Already thrushes from Scandinavia were arriving as they did at the start of every winter, and the bees noticed that squirrels were storing acorns and other nuts much earlier than usual. When the bees reported to Queen Vanessa what was happening outside, she flapped her wings and shivered and reminded them of the old saying, "WHEN SQUIRRELS EARLY START TO HOARD, WINTER WILL STRIKE LIKE A SWORD."

The shorter days and long nights turned the minds of the bees to entertainment. The hive had a good choir with a long collection of folk songs. Most of the songs were based on buzzing noises which could rise and fall

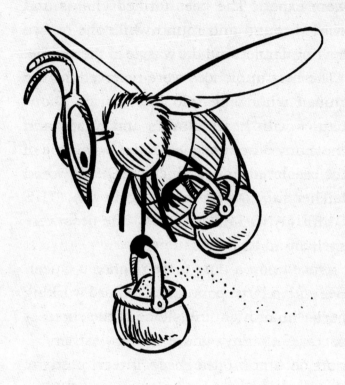

in pitch to produce a pleasing tune. Some of these tunes imitated the warbling of song birds, while others were based on natural sounds such as babbling brooks and the rustle of leaves. There were songs which were accompanied by dancing at which the bees were expert. The bees formed chains and twirled round and round while one or two leading dancers did the waggle in the middle.

The best audiences were reserved for the Queen when she told her stories about battles with hosts of ants and wasps and the many other enemies of the bees. One of the best loved stories which the Queen would tell her subjects again and again was, "THE QUEEN AND THE SPIDER." The bees were spellbound as they listened:

"Once upon a time there reigned a Queen Bee with a large population of hard working bees who brought in gallons of the choicest nectar every day, whatever the weather."

At this point the bees interrupted by clapping loudly and uttering cries of delight.

"Then one day a big spider came down and sat beside the Queen and frightened all the subjects away!" The end of the story was greeted with cries of horror and disbelief.

Young and old bees were fond of singing rhymes and their favourite was the following:

Fiddle-de-dee,
Fiddle-de-dee,
The fly has married
The humble bee.

Says the fly, says he,
Will you marry me,
And live with me,
Sweet humble bee.

Says the bee, says she,
I'll live under your wing,
And you'll never know
That I carry a sting.

So when the parson
Had joined the pair,
They both went out
To take the air.

And the fly did buzz
And the bells did ring –
Did you ever hear
So merry a thing?

And then to think
That of all the flies
The humble bee
Should carry the prize.

   While all this home made entertainment was going on, older bees attended to the winter preparations in the hive. They made sure that the brood chamber was well ventilated and dry. The floors were swept clean at regular intervals and all rubbish thrown out. All joints in walls were inspected and any cracks found were sealed. The doorway was narrowed so as to provide a winter passage and keep intruders at bay.

   Early morning frosts heralded the coming of winter. The bees clustered tightly inside the hive. The colder it was outside the tighter their cluster. In that way the bees knew they could survive any degree of cold. Finally they put out a sign at the entrance saying, "DO NOT DISTURB."

The first snow fell towards the end of October that year. A fine sprinkling of white flakes covered the meadow, the bushes and tree branches. More snow fell in the days that followed and there were icy patches on the pond. The cold snap was followed by mild weather when all the snow and ice melted and there were puddles and mud everywhere.

In the New Year there was also a blizzard which piled the snow in drifts under the hive and along the bushes. The bees and their Queen were fast asleep in the hive dreaming of warm days, flowers and trees in blossom. They dreamt of large flowers full of nectar and pollen and of sparkling dew drops on ferns and blades of grass. So already in mid-winter they dreamt of nature coming to life again and they dreamt of spring.

CHAPTER TEN

THE FIGHT TO SURVIVE

Meanwhile in the new hive, the worker bees cleaned hundreds of cells in the brood chamber. They begged Queen Bella to start laying eggs to expand the colony for the winter months. And the Queen obliged laying eggs in their thousands. So things went according to plan. And in just a few weeks after moving to their new home in the council house garden, Queen Bella was surrounded by crowds of young bees.

Soon they began attending classes to learn the crafts of the hive. They learnt how to forage and be economical with the stocks of honey and pollen. They learnt, above all, bee language.

Feeding so many mouths used up a lot of fresh nectar and pollen; and all through

September and early October the bees made frantic attempts to make good the dwindling stocks with some measure of success. But most flowers were withering and dying in late October because of early morning frosts. So that quite soon the bees were forced to give up foraging to conserve their energy.

Then Queen Bella was advised by her trusted councillors that the stock of honey in the hive was dangerously low and might not last until the nectar flow began again which might not be until April. The bees knew that a mild winter and early spring were their only hope of survival.

Then word went round that the ivy, the evergreen climbing shrub was in flower later than usual and there was a good supply of nectar there. The bees sprang into action and gathered a few more precious pounds of nectar for their stores.

A general meeting was held in the hive in late October at which Queen Bella made a rallying speech to her subjects about the dangers they faced until next spring. She said that all shows and entertainment would be banned during the winter months. The worker bees vowed then to eat as little as possible during the coming months. They pledged themselves to die rather than see their Queen starve to a dreadful death.

The winter came early and the snow covered the council house garden. An old man with grey hair swept the snow away from the hive from time to time. He looked thoughtful whenever he stood in front of the hive. But the bees were fast asleep in a tight cluster and, like their sisters elsewhere, were dreaming of flowers, sunshine and spring. But spring when it came at last, was wet and windy. Days passed and the bees didn't go out and all the time their stocks of honey were dwindling alarmingly.

Hundreds of bees started to die of cold and starvation; their corpses were thrown out in front of the hive into the wind and the rain. As the weeks passed more bees died of hunger so that soon most of the combs were empty of honey.

One early April morning, Queen Bella and her subjects were woken from their slumbers by an army of ants invading the hive and plundering everything in their path. The last few life-sustaining drops of honey soon vanished for the bees were too weak to put up a fight. They watched sadly and horror-struck as the ants disappeared as quickly as they had arrived.

Without hope, Queen Bella sat stunned on her throne of wax in the middle of the royal chamber. Her ladies-in-waiting, who had survived, stayed close by to console her. She remembered the words of her fortune-teller and could not understand why things were ending in such catastrophe.

Suddenly she heard human voices outside the hive. Then, one of her scouts came rushing in to explain that the old man with grey hair, who was known as Mr Hughes, was describing to his grandson Roger the hard and thankless life of the honey bee. He showed Roger an open tin can with a round nail driven into the bottom of it. The can contained sugar syrup. It was warm. "Now I will put the tin on the top bars of the comb frames in the brood chamber inside the hive and cover it with a quilt. If the bees are sensible they'll suck the syrup which, though thick and sticky, is dripping gently where the nail is," he said with a twinkle in his eye.

A general buzz of excitement started in the hive. The strongest worker bees went first and gorged themselves on the syrup. After that they helped their weaker sisters to suck syrup. Nursing bees rushed to the Queen and gave her a good helping. Queen Bella had heard some time in the past that humans believed in miracles. This must be a human miracle, she said to herself. For once, she also remembered with pleasure the old saying about honey and sweetness coming into one's mouth.

The kind old man gave the bees more warm syrup a few days later. Fortified by so much sweetness, the bees went foraging once more. As the weather improved, the stocks

71

of honey and pollen rose in the hive.

Queen Bella looked around her and said to herself, "WHILE THERE'S LIFE, THERE'S HOPE." She began to lay eggs again to the delight of all her subjects. Soon there would be young bees crowding the brood chamber and storage combs above. The hive was alive and safe for another year.

GLOSSARY

A Short List of Unusual Words Used in the Story

AEROBATICS – the rolls and spins of aeroplanes, often seen at air shows

ANTENNA – sensory organ in heads of insects

ASTROLOGER – expert in the art of understanding the influence of stars on life

COMB – beeswax structure of cells for honey or eggs

DRONE – The male honey bee who does no work

LARVA – grub or immature from of insect

MANDIBLE – lower jaw bone of insect

METAMORPHOSIS – change of form from immature insect to adult

NECTAR – sweet liquid produced by flowers

NYMPH – immature insect being hatched

POLLEN – powdery substance discharged by flowers

PROPOLIS – sticky substance obtained from buds or leaves of trees

ROYAL JELLY – white creamy substance on which future queen bee is fed when she is hatching in her cell

SWARM – cluster of bees numbering thousands leaving hive with their Queen to establish new colony of bees in a hive

ZODIAC – a strip of the sky close to the sun's path, divided into twelve parts called the signs of the Zodiac

QUIZ

1. About how many worker bees are there in a strong hive?

2. Do the number of bees in a hive remain the same through the year?

3. How many drones do you expect to find in a colony of bees?

4. Do drones sting when angry?

5. What blossom bearing trees produce nectar? Name at least five

6. How far does a bee fly when foraging?

7. Does a bee drink water?

8. How do you remove a bee sting from your skin?

9. What is a baby queen bee fed on?

10. Who are the enemies of bees? Name at least five

11. What do bees use pollen from flowers for?

12. How long does a worker bee live?

13. How do bees tell each other where nectar bearing flowers are?

14. How do bees talk to one another?

15. Why do bees swarm?

16. What happens to a bee hive in autumn?

17. What do bees do in winter?

18. How do bees produce wax?

19. What is wax used for in a hive?

20. What is a waggle?

ANSWERS

1. From 40,000 to 50,000. 2. No, the number of bees decreases in winter through deaths and cold. 3. One or two hundred. 4. No, because they don't have a sting. 5. Horse chestnut, lime, pear, apple, cherry, plum, oak and sycamore. 6. About 3 km is the limit. 7. Yes. 8. By scraping with finger nail or blade of a knife. 9. Royal jelly. 10. Wasps, hornets, ants, moths, spiders, swallows, mice. 11. They mix pollen with nectar and feed it to the bee larvae. 12. Three months when working in summer but longer in winter. 13. By dancing and flapping their wings so that they buzz. 14. With their antennae and buzzing sounds. 15. Bees swarm in spring or summer to form a new colony. 16. Bees prepare for winter by sealing cracks and storing honey. 17. Bees hibernate in winter except for flights out of the hive to clean themselves. 18. They eat honey then sweat it out as wax. 19. Wax is used for making combs and capping honey or brood cells. 20. The waggle is the dance that bees perform in order to pass information about the location of flowers.